Chad Is the Champ

Chad

Chet

Written by Barbara Levadi
Illustrated by Ian Forss

Chad wanted to win a sketching contest. There was a prize for the best sketch. He made a plan. He chose his pet chimp, Chet, to sketch.

"Come here, Chet," said Chad. "I want to make a sketch of you. Come sit on the bench."

3

Chad told Chet to sit still.
But Chet had an itch.
He scratched and scratched.

"Stop that," said Chad.
"You must sit still.
I cannot make a sketch
if you scratch."

Chet would not sit still.

"You are such a bad chimp," said Chad.
"If you sit still I will give you a chip
to munch."

Crunch, crunch.
Chet chomped on the chip.

After Chet munched on the chip
he jumped from the bench.
He jumped onto a big chest.

"Bad chimp," said Chad.
"Get back on the bench
before I get mad."

Chad chased after Chet.
He had to chase Chet too much,
so he quit.
Chad chose not to make
a sketch of Chet.

"I will find a new contest," said Chad.

Chad chose to play chess.
And he was the chess champ.